Saint Brigid the Fearless

This story was adapted by author Ann Carroll
and illustrated by Derry Dillon

IRELAND'S BEST KNOWN STORIES
IN A NUTSHELL

Published 2014
Poolbeg Press Ltd

123 Grange Hill, Baldoyle
Dublin 13, Ireland

Text © Poolbeg Press Ltd 2014

A catalogue record for this book is available from the British Library.

ISBN 978 1 78199 927 1

Cover design and illustrations by Derry Dillon
Printed by GPS Colour Graphics Ltd, Alexander Road, Belfast BT6 9HP

This book belongs to

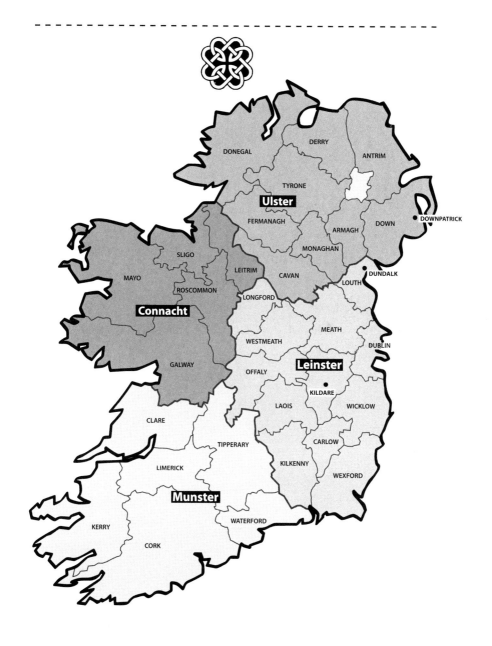

Also in the Nutshell series

Birth

The baby girl was born in 451 A.D. near Dundalk. Although her father, Dubhtach, was a chieftain, her mother, Brocca, was a slave, which made the infant a slave too.

I am a supremely important person, Dubhtach thought, with lots of slaves who have to do whatever I say. So satisfying!

1

This supremely important person was amazed to have a vivid dream about his latest, insignificant possession. In this dream three Christian priests surrounded him and insisted: "You must call the baby Brigid."

Not used to taking orders, even in a dream, Dubthach snapped, "I'll call her what I like!"

At this the priests wailed: "Brigid, Brigid – she must be called Brigid!"

They kept this up all night and when at last Dubhtach woke, his head was splitting and he moaned, "Brigid it is. I can't go through all that again."

Childhood

As a child Brigid had to work hard. From morning till night she looked after the cattle and sheep on her father's land and toiled in the fields and the orchards. But she loved Nature and was content.

Spring was her favourite season, when new life appeared everywhere. The lambs and calves delighted her and it was magical to see fresh buds and leaves appear on the apple and pear trees.

She was a happy child and when she saw unhappy people she wanted to help them. There were lots of poor folk that time in Leinster. They roamed the countryside looking for food and shelter and it didn't take them long to hear about the small girl who always found a way to help.

"She's a slave," they'd tell each other in wonder. "And she's very young. But she never turns anyone away!"

And Brigid would give them fruit, or milk and bread, or sometimes meat and vegetables.

Miracles

Once when there was none of these things to hand she told an old woman, "I'm sorry. All I have is the butter my mother churned this morning."

"Butter is better than nothing," said the old woman and Brigid gave her the huge tub her mother had spent so many hours making.

The old woman staggered off, delighted, and Brigid thought: Mother will be angry, but it can't be helped!

Later, when Brocca went to fetch her butter, Brigid waited outside the dairy, expecting sound and fury. But, when her mother appeared, she looked somewhat dazed.

"I don't understand it." Brocca shook her head as if trying to clear her mind.

"I can explain," Brigid said.

"Can you? I don't think so! I set one tub of butter down on the table and now there are three. Three! I defy anyone to explain that!"

"But there shouldn't be any, Mother. I gave what you made to an old woman."

Brocca gazed at her in wonder. "A few funny things have been happening lately," she said at last. "Nice things, like that sick calf getting well and one of the apple trees suddenly doubling its fruit. And I've noticed they happen after you've been kind to someone." She paused and then said solemnly, "I think these are miracles, Brigid, and they happen because of you."

"That's good, then. Isn't it, Mother?"

"It is, Brigid. As Christians we believe in miracles. But your father is a pagan. He wouldn't be a bit happy to find our god is more powerful than all of his gods put together. Better to say nothing."

The Silent Sisters

Brigid's fame grew. As she got older the sick began to visit her. They came, miserable with ill health, and often left without their crutches and stretchers, bounding with energy and cheerfulness.

One day she cured two young sisters who were mute, touching their throats with her hand. At once they tested their new voices – whispers rising to shrieks of joy. They whooped, bellowed and roared – shouted, laughed and cackled. It was only when they tried singing that Brigid asked them to stop, for neither could hold a note.

Calm at last, they said, "It's wonderful to have our voices. Thank you so much!"

"It's God you must thank," she told them and they went away praising God and telling everyone they met about Brigid.

Dubhtach's Plans

Dubhtach began to hear some of the stories and came to see his daughter. He hadn't visited in a long while.

She's very beautiful, he thought. And while she has been an excellent worker, that cannot last with all these people interrupting her. I'll marry her off to a wealthy man who'll pay well for the privilege.

"It's time to arrange your future, daughter!" he said.

"Yes, it is," Brigid agreed. "I wish to follow a Christian life."

"Your wishes don't matter. I will arrange a wealthy and powerful marriage for you."

"I won't be marrying, Father," Brigid said. "I've made a vow to God to follow the religious life."

"Well, you can unmake your vow!" Dubhtach snapped. "You'd no right to make it. You're my slave – my property – and you'll do what I say!"

By now his face was so red he looked fit to burst and was dancing up and down in fury. Brigid thought it best to say no more for the present.

Weeks later her father returned with a rich young man who took one look at the girl and said, "You'll make me a fine wife."

"No, I won't," Brigid told him. "I'm not marrying anyone."

"Don't start all that again!" spluttered Dubhtach.

The young man was gazing at her. "You're immensely beautiful," he murmured.

Oh God, she prayed, make me look so ugly that this fellow and any other fellow will definitely not want to marry me!

Then she saw the young man's fond gaze turn to horror as huge sores appeared all over her face, which swelled like a balloon. He ran away so fast he couldn't be seen for the dust.

The Other Suitors

Her father tried a few more suitors. They were equally appalled, not only at the thought of marrying such an ugly person, but of paying good gold for the privilege. The last one paused long enough to give Dubhtach a good telling-off.

"You have some nerve!" he spat. "I've a good mind to complain to the king." Then he legged it to his horse.

Dubhtach gave up. "You're free to do what you want," he told Brigid.

A New Life

His daughter took him at his word, said goodbye
to Brocca and, as soon as she left to follow her
destiny, her face stopped swelling, the sores
disappeared and she was beautiful again.

Along the way others joined her. When she got to Kildare she built a small oratory for prayer. One of her visitors was Saint Mel and it is said he ordained her as bishop. There too she met Saint Patrick and Saint Columcille and they became great friends.

Brigid by now had many followers and needed a place for them to live. After much thought she went to the King of Leinster.

Brigid's Cloak

"I need you to give me enough land so I can build two abbeys, one for women and one for men, and grow enough food for all who live there," she told the king.

"Really?" He was highly sarcastic. "And I suppose you want the land for free."

"Yes, thank you," Brigid said.

"Well, you're not getting it!" said the king. "I fought long and hard for all I own – why would I hand any of it over to you?"

"For the glory of God," said Brigid. "We'll be spending our days in prayer and doing good works and growing food. And the poor will be able to rest with us instead of roaming your land."

"Mmm," said the king, not quite convinced, but tempted all the same by this last notion. "It's true the poor can be a terrible nuisance to the rich. How much land do you want?"

"Oh, only as much as my cloak will cover!" Brigid said.

He looked at her and looked at her cloak and sniggered. "Well, I can give you that much, I promise, though I think your abbeys will be tiny."

"Don't you worry about that." Brigid took off her cloak and spread it on the ground. Immediately the cloth began to stretch out in all directions until it covered many, many acres.

Being a Christian, the king, though he wasn't a bit pleased, took the miracle as a sign from God and kept his promise.

Achievements

So Brigid built her abbeys. She helped the sick and the poor and made sure the land was used properly to support the whole community. No one who came looking for help was ever turned away.

She also founded a School of Art, producing metalwork and works of illumination, which were beautifully illustrated books.

The Book of Kildare was created there, said to be as beautiful as the famous Book of Kells. Unfortunately it disappeared more than three hundred years ago, probably destroyed during the religious troubles of that time.

Brigid's Cross

One of her lasting legacies is the simple but beautiful Brigid's Cross.

The story goes that, sitting at the bedside of a dying pagan man and perhaps feeling she'd said enough prayers, Brigid looked around for something to do. The floor of his hut had been swept and was covered with clean rushes. Taking some of these, Brigid wove them into a distinctive cross.

The man's eyes flickered. "What's that?" he wondered.

Brigid told him the story of Christ's life and death. It is said the sick man was so moved he asked to be converted.

Death and Remembrance

At the age of seventy-five Brigid died. She was buried in front of the high altar of her abbey. But, even in death, she couldn't rest. She was exhumed, brought to Downpatrick and placed beside the bodies of Saint Patrick and Saint Columcille.

Her skull went even farther afield, taken to Lisbon by two noblemen. And there it is kept today, in the church of São João Batista, in Lumiar, near Lisbon Airport.

The 1st of February is her Feast Day and on that day in many primary schools children still make Saint Brigid crosses and bring them home, where they are said to protect the family from harm.

Brigid is remembered as the great saint of Spring. She is a reminder that life, no matter how humbly it starts, brings many possibilities.

The End

How to Make a Saint Brigid's Cross

You Will Need

9 reeds (or drinking staws) 8-12 inches long

4 small rubber bands

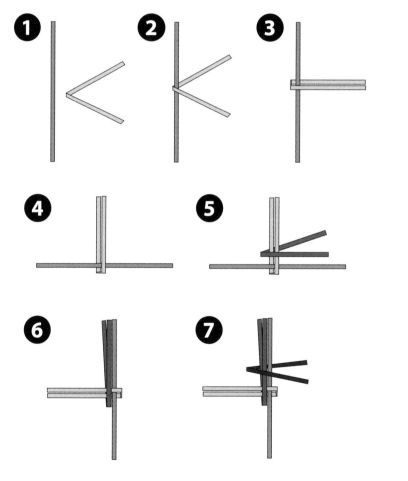

What to Do

Following the diagrams:

1   Take 2 straws. Fold one in half.

2   Put the first straw into the fold of the second straw.

3   Hold the place where the straws overlap tightly between your thumb and forefinger.

4   Turn the 2 straws, held together, so that the ends of the second straw are pointing upwards.

5   Fold a third straw in half. Hook it around the two legs of the second straw, so it lies along half of the first straw.

6   Hold the centre tightly, and turn the 3 straws so that the ends of the third straw are pointing upwards.

7   Fold a fourth straw in half. Hook it around the other straws that are pointing upwards.

8   Repeat the process, rotating all the straws and adding a new folded straw each time.

9   When you have used all 9 straws, tie the ends of the arms of the cross with elastic bands.

10   Trim the rough ends to make them all the same length.

And your cross is ready!

Word Sounds

(Opinions may differ regarding pronunciation)

Words	Sounds
Dubhtach	Dove-tok
Brocca	Brocka
Brigid	Bridge-id
Columcille	Colm-kill
São	Sow-n
João	Ju-ow-n (the 'j' is like the 's' in 'measure')
Batista	Ba-tees-ta

Also available from the **IN A NUTSHELL** series
All you need to know about Ireland's best loved stories in a nutshell

The Story of Newgrange

The Salmon of Knowledge

The Story of Saint Patrick

How Cúchulainn Got His Name

The Children of Lir

The Story of The Giant's Causeway

Granuaile The Pirate Queen

Oisin and Tir na nOg

The Story of Brian Boru

Deirdre of the Sorrows

Heroes of the Red Branch Knights

The Adventures of the Fianna

The Adventures of Maebh
The Warrior Queen

Diarmuid and Gráinne and the Vengeance of Fionn

If you enjoyed this book from
Poolbeg why not visit our website:

www.poolbeg.com

and get another book delivered straight
to your home or to a friend's home.

All books despatched within 24 hours.

POOLBEG

Why not join our mailing list
at www.poolbeg.com and get some
fantastic offers, competitions,
author interviews and much more?

@PoolbegBooks